THANK YOU

This book helps us to understand cancer and empowers us to know how to make a difference.

Mr. C the Globetrotter

by Eva Grayzel

*Dedicated to children who have
a family member with cancer.*

Special thanks to Paul Fallaha, Mr. C illustrator,
Patricia Arberg, graphic designer and friend,
professional and non-professional editors:
Abby Grayzel, Elena Cohen, Elinor Grayzel, Elizabeth Babbin,
Ellie Nadler, Constance Arcury and Patricia Arberg.

Talk4Hope

FAMILY BOOK SERIES

helping children understand cancer

www.Talk4Hope.com

Mr. C the Globetrotter
Copyright © 2013 Talk4Hope
4245 Farmersville Court, Easton, Pennsylvania 18045
Contact & special orders: eva@evagrayzel.com

Printed in Pennsylvania

Grayzel, Eva
Mr. C the Globetrotter/Eva Grayzel

Library of Congress Control Number: 2013934054

ISBN 978-0-9823857-2-2

Cancer, Juvenile Literature
1. Cancer
2. Family
3. Communication
4. Children's Writing

Publisher Talk4Hope
Design by PatADigital Designs
Mr. C illustrations by Paul Fallaha
Back cover photo by Jeremy Cohen
Selected photographs from iStockphoto

**Proceeds from this book help fund Six-Step Screening.
To learn more visit sixstepscreening.org.**

Hi. I'm Mr. C.
The C is short for Cancer.

No one likes to speak my name.
Some people whisper it.

But, I'm no secret.

I live in every country, every
city and every neighborhood,
but not in every person.

I visit families all over the globe.

I've been as far north as Greenland and as far south as New Zealand.

I've been to many countries
around the world.

Have you heard of these places?

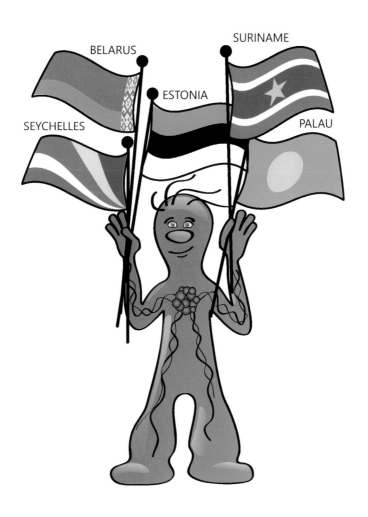

SURINAME

BELARUS

ESTONIA

SEYCHELLES

PALAU

I've seen the seven
Wonders of the World.

I'm glad you want to
learn about me.

The more you know...
the stronger,
wiser
and more helpful
you will be,
in case I come to live with
someone you care about.

I disrupt lives.
I change plans and schedules.

Come with me.
See what I'm talking about.

Meet the Martin family.

Mason Martin has a runny nose and a cough. His cold is contagious. He washes his hands often to prevent spreading his germs. If he rests, the virus will go away in a few days.

Mason's mom is sick, too. Her
illness is different because of me.
However I'm not contagious.

I can't jump,

travel   or

pass

from one person to another. But
I hang around a lot longer than a
virus. Sometimes, I hang around
for only a few months. Sometimes,
I hang around for a few years.

I don't make his mother feel rotten
all the time, like Mason feels when
he has a cold.

I can see Mrs. Martin's heart. It pounds strongly for her children whom she loves more than anything in the whole wide world. She wants them to feel safe and secure.

However, I get tangled in her feelings and affect her mood.

"Mason, stop teasing Monroe. Both of you go to your rooms until you can be nice to each other."

Lately, Mrs. Martin loses her temper easily.

It is hard for the whole family when I come to visit. Everyone has to pitch in a little more and take on extra responsibilities.

I'm a pain in the neck. But I can't be ignored. Everyone has to learn how to deal with me.

Meet children from around the world and

catch a glimpse of how they cope
... when I visit.

I'm Matias from Brazil.
My name means "gift from God."

We never know if it will be a good
day for Dad or not. He tells me
my hugs are medicine.

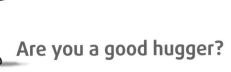

Are you a good hugger?

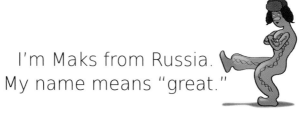

I'm Maks from Russia.
My name means "great."

When my mother feels miserable
from treatments, I say:

I'm sorry you have cancer.
I'm sorry you're in pain.
I'm sorry treatment is rough.

How do you show sympathy?

I'm Malin from Hawaii.
My name means "peaceful."

My aunt is not the same since her
diagnosis. I give her good back rubs.

How can you show you care?

I'm Marceline from Canada.
My name means "young warrior."

Cancer has changed my grandpa.
He smiles, pretending he feels
okay. I put on the same strong
mask and say, "I love you."

Do you say "I love you" often?

I'm Mel from Australia.
My name means "honey."

I wish for a magic wand to
make my brother's cancer
disappear. On rough days,
I call my grandmother.

Who would you call?

I'm Masako from Japan.
My name means "justice."

Mom has cancer and I'm scared.
After talking to my therapist,
I feel peace in my heart.

Who can you share feelings with?

I'm Mohana from India.
My name means "enchanting."

My sister gets a lot of attention
because she has cancer. Luckily,
I have friends who give me
attention when my family can't.

Who are your special friends?

I'm Mkombozi from Tanzania.
My name means "emancipator."

Ever since Mom got cancer, I stay
close to home. Drawing keeps me
busy. Mom smiles every time she
sees my art hanging on the wall.

Can your art make someone smile?

I'm Munya from Morocco.
My name means "wish or desire."

When my dad has energy, we
dance. When he doesn't, we listen
to music. I'm always searching for
new songs we can enjoy together.

**What activity would
you do together?**

I'm Margit from Sweden.
My name means "pearl."

I do what I can to make life easier
while Mom is having radiation and
chemotherapy. I wash dishes, fold
laundry and bring her water to stay
hydrated. Mom always takes such
good care of me. Now, I can take
care of her.

How can you help?

I'm Manton from Namibia.
My name means "sandy earth."

I'm always thinking about Dad. My teacher knows why I have a hard time focusing. I don't want my parents to worry about my grades, so I get help with homework.

Who can you ask for help?

I'm Mab from Ireland.
My name means "happy."

When my best friend can attend
school, I wear a bandana to show
support. When she feels well
enough, I invite her for sleepovers.

I'm her "BFF"♡Best Friend Forever♡
and that's what best friends do!

**What can you do
for a friend with cancer?**

I'm Milek from Poland.
My name means "lover of glory."

My brother has cancer. I pray for
courage, strength, friendship and
lots of hugs for our whole family.

My prayers make a difference.

Do you pray?

I'm Morgan from New Zealand.
My name means "sea-born."

I used to mope around feeling sad
about Dad's cancer. Now, I pull out
my joke book and crack a good
one! Cancer doesn't stop us from
laughing!

Ha! Ha!
Ha!
Ha!

Can you tell a funny joke?

Sometimes, Mr. C visits kids like me.

I'm Malva from Belize.
My name means "delicate."

I'm optimistic my cancer will be
gone soon. I always feel better
after writing down my feelings.

Dear Diary

Do you have a diary to write in?

Have you had enough globetrotting?
I have! I want a break from traveling!

Until a cure is found,
I have no choice.

I turn life upside down,
but I try to make up for it.

When I visit, families bond and
communities come together.
Everyone learns new ways to
cope with life's challenges.

My name is Mr. C. The C stands for Cancer. Remember, cancer is just a word. It means a person is sick. It doesn't mean a person will die.

I MAKE A LOT OF NOISE

With your help, the noise can be music.

Do you see the first three letters in the word "cancer?"

You CAN make a difference.

Your calls, letters, pictures and time
spent together is medicine...

for a better week,
a better day,
a better moment.

Thank you for taking the time
to get to know me better.

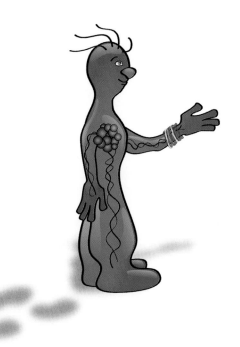

Notes

About Cancer

Cancer isn't 'catchy' like a cold.
Everyone experiences cancer differently.
Feelings about cancer are often hard to identify and discuss.
Sharing feelings helps others understand.
Treatment may cure cancer but cause other challenges.
A person is a survivor once diagnosed.

For Children

Don't be afraid to ask questions.
Express feelings in a diary or a drawing.
Give hugs, accept hugs and say "I love you."
Send a card - include a joke, picture or prayer.
Smile, laugh and enjoy time together.
Ask, "What can I do to bring you happiness?"

For Parents

Illness is a unique opportunity to teach values to children.
Ask children specific questions. ("Is a hospital visit scary?")
Do something nice for the caregivers to renew their energy.
Acknowledge and emphasize life's gifts.
Flip through a photo album and share family "name" stories.
Partake in a community service activity together.
Inform teachers of the illness. Seek out a child therapist.

Talk4Hope

FAMILY BOOK SERIES

helping children understand cancer

www.Talk4Hope.com

Talk more about this book...

Visit Talk4Hope.com

SWEDEN
Margit

POLAND
Milek

IRELAND
Mab

MOROCCO
Munya

CANADA
Marceline

HAWAII
Malin

U.S.A.
Martin Family

SURINAME

BELIZE
Malva

BRAZIL
Matias

RUSSIA
Maks

ESTONIA

BELARUS

JAPAN
Masako

INDIA
Mohana

PALAU

SEYCHELLES

AUSTRALIA
Mel

TANZANIA
Mkombozi

MIBIA
anton

NEW ZEALAND
Morgan

About the Author

Eva Grayzel is a nationally recognized Master Storyteller and expert on interactive storytelling techniques. To celebrate her 10-year cancer free anniversary, Eva founded the Talk4Hope family book series. Mr. C, in the book *Mr. C Plays Hide & Seek*, was such a comfortable way to introduce cancer to children, Eva followed it with this book, *Mr. C the Globetrotter*. A third book is in the works about how teenagers cope when Mr. C comes to visit families.

Note from the Author

My children were five and seven years old when I was diagnosed with cancer. They were deeply affected by watching me struggle with the severe effects of treatment. Their fear of losing me was deep, real and bottled. I regret not seeking professional counseling for them during that time.

I wrote the Talk4Hope Family Book Series to help children under-stand cancer, acknowledge their feelings, and empower them with ways to make a difference. *Mr. C the Globetrotter* addresses coping skills and communication strategies, everything I wish my children had during that difficult time. In *Mr. C Plays Hide & Seek*, Mr. C reveals the rules of his game and with whom he plays.

Why do all the names begin with "M"? "Hmmmmmm" is the sound of thinking. I hope readers will think about how they can help themselves and others. Also, "M" is the main letter in the word "MOM." During difficult days, my children gave me a reason to survive and thrive. Cancer is an opportunity to provide family and friends with a legacy of courage, gratitude and compassion.

About Me

My name is _____

My name means _____

My favorite child in this book is _____

Why? _____

Do you know anyone who has or had cancer?_____

What are their names? _____

What can you do to show you care? _____

_____

One day, I'd like to visit these countries: _____

_____

What blessings in life outweigh cancer? _____

_____

Reader's Notes

EXPERIENCE THE STORY

inspires . motivates . transforms
through the power of story

Motivational Speaker
Master Storyteller

Survivorship Event

Children of Survivors Program

Student and Family Education

www.EvaGrayzel.com

Book Eva for your next event/conference!
programs@evagrayzel.com